I Like Stripes

by Deborah Schecter

ISBN-13: 978-0-545-25689-6 / ISBN-10: 0-545-25689-5

Illustrated by Anne Kennedy
Designed by Maria Lilja • Colored by Ka-Yeon Kim-Li
Copyright © 2010 by Deborah Schecter

■SCHOLASTIC

A candy cane has stripes.
I like stripes.

Toothpaste has stripes.
I like stripes.

A flag has stripes.
I like stripes.

A zebra has stripes.
I like stripes.

A street has stripes.
I like stripes.

A ladybug has stripes.
No! No! No!

A ladybug has spots.
I like spots!